INCAS
◁ MYTHS AND LEGENDS ▷

Translated *by* Frances Halton
Illustrations *by* Jean Torton
Original version *by* Danièle Küss
Edited *by* Gilles Ragache

CHERRYTREE BOOKS

A Cherrytree Book

Adapted by A S Publishing
from *Les Incas*, published by Hachette

First published 1991
by Cherrytree Press Ltd
a subsidiary of
The Chivers Company Ltd
Windsor Bridge Road
Bath, Avon BA2 3AX

British Library Cataloguing in Publication Data
Incas.
  1. Myths. Legends. Inca myths. Inca legends.
  Inca myths & legends.
  I. Halton, Frances   II. Series   III. Incas.
  English
  398.20985

  ISBN 0-7451-5122-1

Printed in Hong Kong by Colorcraft Ltd

CONTENTS

THE FIRST INCAS

Before the Incas came to Earth, the people they were to rule were like wild animals. They lived among steep, scrub-covered mountains; they had no houses or villages, no religion and no law. They took shelter in caves and fed on roots and berries.

One day their creator, the sun god, took pity on these sad creatures. He decided to send his son Ayar Manco and his daughter Mama Ocllo to help them. He called his children to him and said:

'Tomorrow at dawn you must go down to Earth and build a new empire there. You must teach its people civilized ways. Show them how to tame animals, and how to grow plants, weave, and make tools and jewels. Explain the laws that will allow them to live together peacefully. Above all, you must tell them that I am the god who has created them and given them all good things, and that they must never cease to worship me.'

'Before you can do all this,' the sun god went on, 'you must found a great capital city with a temple to me, and from this centre you can set out to the north and south to conquer your empire.'

Ayar Manco and Mama Ocllo listened carefully to their father. They asked him where they should found the capital of the new Inca empire.

'Take this golden rod,' said their father. 'You will find a great lake. From there, travel north. Each time you stop to eat or sleep, try to push the rod into the ground. When it will go in without any trouble, you will have arrived at the site of your capital, Cuzco.'

The next morning, Ayar Manco and Mama Ocllo arrived beside Lake Titicaca, just as the sun rose above the horizon. They were splendidly dressed, and their golden ornaments shone like stars. The savage people realized that they were gods. They decided to follow them at a distance, to see why they had come to Earth.

Ayar Manco and Mama Ocllo set out to the north. They travelled for many days, but they could not stop because their golden rod would not sink into the soil. One sunny morning, they came to a beautiful valley surrounded by majestic mountains. Yet again they tried to push their rod into the ground, and to their astonishment it sank deep into the earth.

By now dozens of wild people were watching the first Incas. Ayar Manco said to his sister: 'This is where our father the sun wished us to found our capital. We must explain his wishes to these savages; then they can help us build our city.'

Soon the savages came to trust the children of the sun, and decided to help them build the better world they had described so well.

Ayar Manco and Mama Ocllo dazzled the savage Indians with their magnificent clothes and ornaments.

Ayar Manco tethers the sun to stop it setting until he has built his capital, Cuzco.

THE CREATION OF CUZCO

Ayar Manco and Mama Ocllo gave a sigh of relief when they saw their golden rod sink into the ground at Cuzco. They set to work with the savages who had joined them to build their great capital.

Immediately they ran into difficulties. Such a strong wind blew across the site that even the largest rocks that they could carry were whirled away like fallen leaves. What could be done? Ayar Manco had an idea. They lured the wind into the llamas' enclosure and shut it up there. At last work could begin in earnest.

Just as the great temple was completed, Ayar Manco's brother Ucho arrived from the far-away plains where he lived.

'What are you doing here?' asked Ayar Manco. 'I know you hate mountains.'

'That's true,' replied Ayar Ucho, 'but I cannot bear to hear the wails and groans coming day and night from the llamas' enclosure. Who have you shut up there?'

'That's the wind,' said Ayar Manco nervously. 'It was stopping us from building the city as our father the sun wishes. I simply must shut it up until we have finished.'

Ayar Ucho was furious. 'You have no right to treat my friend the wind like that!' he said. 'This evening at sunset I shall come back to release him.'

Ayar Manco said nothing. He could never complete the marvellous city he had imagined by the end of the day. Then he had another clever idea. He asked the strongest of his servants to go with him to the top of the mountain. As the sun passed them, they caught it and anchored it to a huge rock. Try as it might it could not travel on, and since the sun did not set Ayar Manco could finish his city.

As soon as the last stone was firmly in place, Ayar Manco let loose first the sun and then the wind, which rushed off as fast as it could for fear of being trapped again. Then Ayar Manco and Mama Ocllo married each other, and founded the first Inca dynasty. Ayar Manco took the name Manco Capac.

THE INCAS AND THEIR EMPIRE

The Incas were members of a group of families who came from Cuzco, high up in the Andes mountains in Peru. They settled there around AD 1100 under their leader Manco Capac. During the 15th century they built up a vast empire by conquering the neighbouring tribes of Indians.

The term 'Inca' is used to describe the members of the family, who were the ruling class of the empire and who had special privileges. The emperor is known as the Inca. The Incas and the Indians they ruled shared many of the same myths and legends.

Cuzco remained the capital and centre of the Inca empire. At its height, in the early 16th century, it was the equal of the great European cities of the time, with more than 200,000 inhabitants. But this great city and the whole empire were destroyed in the mid 16th century by Spanish adventurers greedy for gold.

THE SHEPHERD AND THE SUN'S DAUGHTER

Acoyanapa guarded the special llamas which *the Inca* sacrificed to the sun. One day as he walked behind his flock, playing a delightful tune on his flute, Acoyanapa met two beautiful girls. He recognized them at once as two of the 'virgins of the sun', who served the god in a temple not far away.

As soon as they saw each other, Acoyanapa and one of the girls fell deeply in love. Her name was Chuquillanto, and she could hardly tear herself away from him when evening fell and she had to go back to the temple. She shut herself in her room and cried all night as she thought about him.

From that time on all the beauties and luxuries of the temple meant nothing to Chuquillanto. She lay in her room and pined away for love of her shepherd. One day she had a strange dream; in it, a bird flew on to her knee and said:

'Pretty princess, cry no longer. If you wish to see your shepherd again, go to the heart of the temple, to the four fountains from which flow the rivers which water the four provinces of the

8

Acoyanapa entered and left the temple with Chuquillanto in the form of the stick.

One day a guard came across the lovers. They fled from the temple, but the guard followed them. The shepherd knew all the paths, but the girl could not run fast enough to shake off their pursuer. When he was on the point of capturing her, there was a great clap of thunder, and the earth began to shake. The trees were tossed in all directions and rocks crashed down the mountain slopes, destroying everything in their path. Meanwhile, the lovers had reached the mountain summit. As they did so, an intense light filled the sky, and the lovers were transformed into two rocks, leaning against each other. And so they remained together until the end of time.

Sitting among the sacred springs,
Chuquillanto sings of her love for Acoyanapa.

empire. Seat yourself in the centre of the four fountains, think of Acoyanapa as hard as you can, and sing a song in his memory. If the fountains sing with you, your wish will be fulfilled.'

Chuquillanto woke up with a start, dressed quickly, and made her way to the springs at the heart of the temple. As soon as she began to sing, the waters echoed her song. The next day, she ran to the place where she and the shepherd had met. He was nowhere to be seen, but instead Chuquillanto found his mother. In her hand was a carved stick, the height of a man. Chuquillanto felt a strange desire to own this stick. The old woman could refuse nothing to a virgin of the sun!

Sadly, Chuquillanto returned to the temple and went to bed. She placed her stick beside her and began to cry. At once the stick was turned into Acoyanapa! The couple decided never again to be parted, and from then on

THE ANGER OF THE THUNDER GOD

Inti Illapa the thunder god was in a very bad temper. All the sacrifices offered by the villages around were not enough to soothe him. Darker and darker storm clouds gathered around his head, and lightning streaked from his eyes. He ground and gnashed his teeth with rage. The terrified Indians gathered round their fires to pray and sing new hymns to Inti Illapa. They both loved and feared him, because he made their fields fertile or destroyed their crops, according to his mood.

At the foot of the mountain, a frail, bent Indian was walking quickly through the storm. He was terrified of being struck by lightning; if he were, he would have to slave for ever in the great barns of the thunder god. Once before this had happened to him, but he had managed to escape. He remembered vividly his terrifying capture and imprisonment. A storm had broken out while he guarded his flock of llamas on the mountain slopes. As he sheltered under a rock, strange figures came whirling towards him. He heard snakes hissing around his head; then a terrible chill came over him and he lost consciousness.

When he came to, he was lying on a pile of straw in a barn. Close by was a huddled group of men in rags. He realized immediately that he was in the barn of the thunder god. He managed to escape during a particularly violent storm, but this memory haunted him as he walked through the rain.

Suddenly he saw a gleam of light. He walked more quickly and soon he could see a house, from within which came a faint glimmer. A very old woman with white hair and a deeply wrinkled face came to the door as she heard his approach.

'Don't come in!' she cried in terror. 'If my

sons find you here, they will carry you off.'

'Who are your sons?' asked the Indian with interest.

'They would punish me fearfully if I told you,' she whispered.

'I do not know where else to go,' insisted the Indian. 'I am quite exhausted, and I beg you to hide me.'

The old woman took pity on the fugitive, and let him in. She hid him under a pile of covers, and warned him not to move. Suddenly a streak of lightning lit up the room, and after a fearful grinding sound the door opened and a freezing wind blew in. Three young men appeared. They were armed with slings, and carried sacks bulging with maize and beans. These bags were tied with snakes which hissed and flicked out their long forked tongues towards the young Indian. He lay frozen with terror. He recognized the three sons of the thunder god! In time a strange sleep overcame him.

When he woke up, he was lying on damp grass beside a lake. There was no sign of any house. He thought he must have been dreaming, but when he got up, there, under his hand, was a scrap of wool exactly the same colour as the coverlet under which the old woman had hidden him. He picked it up and knotted it round his fist, but he never told anyone where it came from, nor why he never took it off.

The sons of Inti Illapa, the thunder god.

▷ THE LLAMA IN THE SKY ◁

One starry night, a young Indian boy sat at the foot of a tree, sleepily thinking about Yacana. The priests had told him of this heavenly llama who lived in a group of stars. Each night he came to Earth to drink, but no one ever saw him because he walked along the bottom of the river beds. Yacana was immensely tall, they said, and his eyes were as bright as the stars in the sky. His coat was white and, when he leapt up towards the skies, the wind that went with him whistled like the bluebirds in the forest.

Suddenly a cold and dazzling light roused the young Indian. Little by little it took the shape of a llama, which came to rest beside a stream not far from him. The young Indian curled himself up and held his breath as he watched the heavenly creature drinking from the water. As he did so, he felt a gentle touch on his face, then another and another. Tufts of wool were falling about him. He was too afraid to move, and after a time he fell asleep.

When the boy woke up next morning, the llama had disappeared. But the wool which he had felt falling around him was real enough – he was surrounded by heaps of it, in all colours. The boy could not believe his eyes. He was so poor that he did not own a single llama, and this was the chance of a lifetime for him!

Running joyfully to the stream, he vowed that he would venerate it to the end of his days, and that he would worship the constellation of the llama for the rest of his life. Each month he would come back to sacrifice a young llama there. Then he gathered up all the miraculous wool and took it to the town to sell.

Never had the Indians seen such brilliant coloured wool, and everyone wished to buy some. With the money they gave him, the boy bought two llamas. By magic they produced a flock of more than two thousand llamas in a single year.

Since that day Indians often go to the sacred stream to watch for Yacana. It seems that he comes to Earth every midnight, when he is so thirsty that he drinks a great deal of water. The Indians say that it is thanks to him that there are no more floods. If the heavenly llama did not drink so much water, the rivers would flood and the sea level would have risen and drowned the villages long ago.

Near Yacana in the sky are a number of fainter stars. These are his children. Just beside him are three bright stars that the Indians also worship. When these can be seen clearly, crops will ripen; but if they are hardly visible, the harvest will be bad.

Yacana has never returned to the stream. It seems that he never drinks twice at the same place. But ever since that day, if you are near the spring at daybreak, listen for the wind whistling like the little bluebirds of the forest.

STARS AND CONSTELLATIONS
The Incas believed that the constellation we call Lira, the Lyre, represented a llama. It watched over and protected all the llamas on Earth. Many constellations and stars looked after other things on Earth, and so were worshipped by the Incas.

Each night Yacana the llama comes down to drink from Earth's rivers.

▷ CONIRAYA'S SON ◁

Long ago in Peru, there were places or objects inhabited by spirits called *huacas*. Sometimes these spirits took the form of animals or people. One huaca took the form of a beautiful woman called Cauillaca. All the other huacas were in love with her, but she thought that none of them was good enough for her.

One day, as Cauillaca sat weaving, she heard a strange song. She turned and saw a startlingly-beautiful coloured bird nearby. She stole up to look at it, but just as she came within reach it flew away and disappeared. In its place was a luscious fruit which she picked and ate.

A few months later, Cauillaca gave birth to a son. She could not understand this, since she had never had a lover. For a year and more she

puzzled, and then she summoned all the huacas in the country to come to Anchicocha.

When Cauillaca arrived at the gathering, she hid for a few minutes behind a tree and gazed at one huaca after another. She hoped to recognize a likeness between her son and his father. The huacas had taken all sorts of shapes and her look passed over the spirits of water and fire, of trees and rocks, of snakes and vultures – but none had the slightest resemblance to her son. Only one, Coniraya, came in the guise of a poor and tattered Indian.

When all the huacas had arrived, Cauillaca made a speech. 'My friends,' she said, 'I have brought you here to tell you a secret. This little boy beside me is my son! Since I have never had a lover I do not know how this can be. I have called you together today so that my child's father can reveal himself, and then I shall marry him before you all.'

The huacas looked at one another, trying to guess who was responsible. When she realized that no one was going to come forward, Cauillaca spoke again.

'Since all of you are silent, I leave it to my son to show us. He is sure to want his father to lift him up.'

Cauillaca is startled by strange birdsong.

The child looked gravely at each huaca in turn. Then he crawled over to Coniraya, stretched out his arms, and smiled. A wave of shame swept over Cauillaca. Scarlet with anger, she swept her son up in her arms and ran into the forest.

Coniraya transformed himself into a handsome young prince. He had wanted to punish her for her pride; now his only thought was to marry her. 'Wait for me,' he cried. 'Turn and see me as I really am!' But Cauillaca sped on without looking back.

'I shall never be able to face anyone who knows me again,' she wept. 'I could not bear to be despised and mocked by them as the wife of a beggar.'

Coniraya raced after her. Before long he met an eagle. 'Have you seen Cauillaca?' he cried. 'This forest is so thick that I have lost sight of her.'

'She is not far ahead,' replied the eagle. 'If you hurry a little, you will soon catch up with her.'

Coniraya blessed the eagle and said: 'To thank you for such good news, I will give you the right to go anywhere you wish; to fly to the top of the mountains and make your nest in the most inaccessible places. And you shall be

allowed to eat any dead animal that you find, and even to kill and eat any animal that you can catch.'

Coniraya ran on. He met a fox and asked it the same question; but the fox replied that Coniraya had no hope of catching up with Cauillaca. Coniraya cursed the fox in his disappointment, condemning it to stink and to hunt only at night.

A little farther on Coniraya met a puma, who said that Cauillaca had only just passed. Coniraya told the puma: 'You will be feared and respected. You will carry out my justice by killing Indians who do wrong and eating their llamas. At your death people will cure your skin and wear it on sacred feast days.'

On and on ran Coniraya, asking the animals he met where Cauillaca was and cursing or blessing them according to their answers. When he arrived at the sea shore he saw two young girls. He panted: 'Have you seen a beautiful girl with a baby in her arms? I have followed her through the forest, and she cannot be far away.'

'We know Cauillaca well,' they replied, laughing. 'She took refuge with her son in the sea, and they were transformed into rocks. See, there they are!'

Coniraya fell on his knees in the sand. He stayed there until night fell, watching the waves break over the rocks and crying bitterly. His loved ones were there, two paces from him, but he had lost them for ever.

Cauillaca's child looks at the huacas to find his father.

17

THE FIGHT BETWEEN FIRE AND WATER

Huallallo, spirit of fire, and Pariacaca, spirit of water, struggled ceaselessly with each other to rule over the land of Mullococha. When Huallallo had the upper hand it was very hot; but when Pariacaca was winning the land grew cold and hail began to fall.

At last they agreed to have one final battle; whoever won would rule for ever. Pariacaca had been born from five eggs, so he had five separate bodies. As the fight began these five spread out in five different directions, and hurled torrents of water on Huallallo the fire spirit. His flames sank hissing and writhing to the ground, but again and again gathered strength and shot back into the sky like an erupting volcano. Pariacaca was not discouraged; he poured down more and more water. The two contestants were so equally matched that it seemed as though the struggle would never end.

Towards sunset yellow and red rain began to fall, but Huallallo's flames reached up to lick the clouds. The deluges of water that Pariacaca was pouring out threatened to drown the villages of the Indians. With the help of some friendly spirits, they turned a mountain upside down to catch it, and so created the lake of Mullococha. At last Huallallo was swamped by the flood, and one by one his flames went out. But he managed to escape, and fled to the region called Anti. One of Pariacaca's sons followed to stand guard over him, in case he ever wanted to return to take revenge.

Pariacaca had conquered Huallallo once and for all; to complete his victory he now had to defeat Huallallo's wife, who also burned with intense heat. The fight was more difficult than he expected; again he poured out torrents of water with little effect.

Huallallo struggles against the five forms of Pariacaca.

Suddenly Huallallo's wife threw a rock at the leg of one of Pariacaca's sons. He replied with a jet of water so strong that it carried her right down to the sea. Pariacaca's son was badly wounded, and he realized that he would never walk again. He suggested that he should stay beside the sea and make sure that Huallallo's wife too never returned to take her revenge. His father accepted, and ordered the Indians who lived in the region to bring his son a regular supply of corn and young llamas for food. They were happy to do so, for the flames of Huallallo's wife had burned their villages and forests.

Each time fire broke out, the Indians hurried to make sacrifices to appease the anger of the god. Then they prayed at the foot of a sacred rock, round which whistled the spirit of Pariacaca.

▷ VIRACOCHA'S PEOPLE ◁

When the god Viracocha first created the world there were no sun, moon, or stars. He carved and painted giant figures, but just before he gave them life he wondered if he were wise to put such huge people on his world. So he broke up his giants and began work again, being careful to make figures no bigger than himself. Then he brought them to life and told them:

'Never forget me, and worship me to the end of time! Be honest, hardworking and good. Otherwise I shall destroy you.'

For some time they obeyed Viracocha's orders, but little by little they forgot about them. They even forgot Viracocha himself. This made him so angry that he could not bear to look at them. He carried out his threat to destroy them; some he turned into stone, while others were swallowed up in the ground. The rest he drowned in a deluge which flooded all the land.

Viracocha kept three of his first people to help him to make a new world. When the land was quite dry again, he began work. First he made light; standing on the shore of Lake Titicaca, he drew out of it the sun, the moon and the stars. Taking some huge blocks of stone, he carved the different kinds of people who were to live in his new world. Then he gave them souls, and ordered them to go in all directions and choose the regions in which they would like to live. Then he carved the animals and gave them life too.

When his work was done, Viracocha decided to travel round the world and see how his new people were behaving themselves. He arrived at Cacha, but the inhabitants did not recognize him; he looked so different from them that they tried to kill him! They had forgotten him already. Viracocha knelt down and lifted his angry face to the sky; fire swept down and destroyed the village. Then the terrified Indians recognized the god. They ran towards him, begging his forgiveness. They made sacrifices and swore to worship him to the end of time.

Viracocha took pity on his people and stopped the fire with a wave of his rod. To make sure that they would not forget, he left one of the hills nearby to burn for a long time. When the fire died down, the huge stones on the hillside had become so light that a single

Viracocha the creator carved people and animals of stone, then brought them to life.

man could lift them without difficulty, where before several people working together could only just move them. For many years afterwards, the Indians brought offerings to Viracocha to these strange stones.

Viracocha now went down to the ocean to rejoin his servants who had been carrying out his orders elsewhere. Hundreds of men and women went with him to listen to his final words. Viracocha told them that he was leaving for ever, but that he would send them a divine messenger to watch over them and teach them all they needed to know. Then he turned and walked across the waves towards the horizon. Gradually they lost sight of him in the spray. This is why the Indians gave him the name Viracocha, which means 'seaspray'; and for long afterwards they kept watch on the shore for the arrival of his messenger.

INCA GODS

Viracocha was the most important Inca god; he was the creator, who taught his people how to live and work and gave them all they needed. The Incas prayed to him when they were in serious trouble, but he did not play a great part in everyday life.

Inti Illapa was the god of thunder. People often made sacrifices to him and worshipped at his shrines, as he brought rain.

Inti, the sun god, was the ancestor of the Inca dynasty and played the most important part in everyday life. The most magnificent temples and shrines were built for his worship. The importance of their god added to the power of the ruling Inca family. Inti is often portrayed as a golden disc.

Animals were specially reared for sacrifice. These included white llamas for the sun, brown llamas for Viracocha, guinea pigs, and sometimes birds. Offerings of gold and silver, coca leaves, food and cloth were also made. Every year two babies were sacrificed in the most important temples.

The Incas believed that groups of stars, or constellations, watched over and protected everything that had been created. The moon, Mamaquilla, was worshipped as the

sister and wife of the sun.

The Incas believed that sacred objects had spirits called *huacas* associated with them. These huacas were kept in a good mood with offerings. Almost anything – a place such as a cave or mountain, a stone, a tree, a house – could be a huaca.

The Inca emperor was descended from Inti and was looked on as a god. He is shown carrying a carved wooden figure or fetish. Every person had one of these, in which lived their guardian spirit.

▷ RICH AND POOR ◁

In a little village perched on the mountain slopes lived a man called Uathiacuri. He was dressed in rags and ate only charred meat and the berries he could find in the forest. This was strange, for he was the son of the god Pariacaca.

Nearby, at Anchicocha, lived a very rich Indian; his house was roofed over with brightly coloured feathers and its walls were covered with fine cloth. He had a great many llamas which were the envy of all his neighbours.

People came from far away to pay their respects to him and to ask his advice, for they thought he was a god. He was known simply as the Rich Man.

One day, the Rich Man fell ill. He promised a fortune to anyone who could help him, but nothing did him any good. People began to doubt that he was a god, and some even began to curse him.

At this time, poor Uathiacuri was returning

24

from a long journey. On his way he met a fox which said to him:

'I come from Anchicocha, where there is a very rich, very sick man. I know that his wife caused his illness because she is secretly in love with another man, and this has brought a curse on him. Two snakes live on the roof of his house, waiting for him to die so that they can eat him. Under a flat stone in front of the door, a two-headed toad is also waiting for his death.'

Uathiacuri had already heard about the Rich Man who claimed to be a god. He decided to teach him a lesson. When he got to the village, he pretended to know nothing and asked the youngest of the Rich Man's daughters if there were not a sick person at her home. The girl, Champinaca, replied: 'Yes, sir, it is my father.'

Champinaca was so beautiful that Uathiacuri said: 'If you will marry me, I promise that I will save him.' He was so dirty and poor that she hesitated, but she loved her father so much that she accepted Uathiacuri and ran home to tell what had happened to her. The sick man was so desperate that he would try anything.

'You are the victim of an evil curse,' said Uathiacuri, 'and your wife is responsible. Do you know that two enormous snakes are waiting for you to die so that they can eat you? Do you know that there is a two-headed toad under the flat stone by the door, waiting to do the same? If you want to regain your health, you must kill all three. Then you will get better. But when you are completely cured you must thank me by worshipping my father Pariacaca. He is a true god. You must bow down before him to show everyone that you are an imposter.'

The sick man and his friends could not believe their ears, but they went out of the house and found the snakes and the two-headed toad. Just as Uathiacuri had predicted, the Rich

The Rich Man's house was splendidly decorated with carvings and patterned rugs, but snakes and a two-headed toad lurked – waiting for him to die.

Man began to feel better as soon as he had killed the animals. But Champinaca's rich brother-in-law was furious. He could not bear poor Uathiacuri to be treated just the same as himself. One day he went to him and challenged him to a series of contests.

Uathiacuri accepted the challenge at once. 'Until tomorrow!' he cried. Then he went to Condorcoto to talk to his father.

Pariacaca was sitting in one of the five sacred eggs from which, at the beginning of the world, he had been born in five separate bodies. He listened carefully to his son and told him to come to see him between each trial.

Uathiacuri felt very confident as he went back to Anchicocha, and when his brother-in-law told him that the first test would be to see who could drink and dance for longer, he agreed cheerfully. Off he ran to see his father, who gave him a pitcher of chicha beer and a magic flute. Thanks to these Uathiacuri won the contest. His brother-in-law angrily issued another challenge.

'We will see who can produce the most magnificent dress,' he said. 'You won't be able to match me tomorrow.'

Uathiacuri hurried to see his father, who gave him a poncho made of snow. It was so beautiful that no one noticed the cloak of multi-coloured feathers that his brother-in-law was wearing.

For the third test, the rivals were to come to the village square dressed in the skin of a puma. The wearer of the more beautiful skin would be the champion. Again, Uathiacuri ran to see his father, who said: 'Go to the spring at the top of the mountain; there you will find a magnificent red puma skin with which you will win the contest.'

When Uathiacuri arrived in the square, clothed in the extraordinary skin, a rainbow circled his head like a crown. The watching Indians were stunned. His furious brother-in-law produced another test which he felt sure of winning.

'Now,' he said, 'we will have one last contest;

whoever wins this will have won the whole competition. We must each build a house in a single day and night. Whoever builds the better house will be the champion. Start at once; there is no time for you to leave the village before we begin.'

Helped by his many servants, the rich brother-in-law quickly built a splendid house. Poor Uathiacuri, with only his wife to help him, had only built the foundations when night fell. The watching Indians went off to bed; they had no doubts about the winner. But just as they were entering their houses they heard an extraordinary noise. It was made by thousands of birds, snakes and wild llamas carrying stones, branches, shells and wool to help Uathiacuri. By dawn, work was finished; and the Indians had never seen such a beautiful and splendidly decorated house.

Uathiacuri had had enough. He said to his brother-in-law: 'I have done all that you have told me. Now do as I say. We are going to dance in the village square.'

The brother-in-law arrived first as usual, and began to dance. Suddenly Uathiacuri rushed in, and gave a cry which froze the blood of everyone who heard it. The brother-in-law raced off in panic; and just as he reached the wood which surrounded the village he turned into a deer. Then Uathiacuri caused the river to flood and sweep away the Rich Man's house and everyone in it. All that remained was the flat stone beneath which the two-headed toad had hidden, and on this the Indians placed their offerings to the god Pariacaca who watched over them.

Uathiacuri's magnificent red puma skin gave him victory over his rich brother-in-law.

THE RAINBOW

Before the coming of Pachacutec, Hueva was a wild region covered by impenetrable forests. No Indians dared go there. At the edge of the forest was in immense lake, whose waters were black and icy cold. On its banks lived a tribe of giants, called the Huillcas.

One day the chief giant, Turuncana, said to his people: 'This morning in the forest a beautiful young girl came up to me, crying and trembling. She told me that her name is Rainbow, and that she wants our protection from an enormous monkey called Mancharu who has been chasing her for several days.

In the hand of the giant Turuncana, Rainbow is safe from the monkey Mancharu.

28

Then she jumped into my hand, curled up there, and turned herself into a tiny ball of wool; she had seen Mancharu in the treetops. Although we escaped him, he will be following us, so take care. He is very dangerous; red lightning flashes from his eyes, and he growls like thunder. He spits poison which dissolves everything it touches.'

The terrified giants hurried to the caves where they lived, and barricaded the entrances with enormous stones. Months passed without any sign of Mancharu, but Turuncana never slept; he felt sure that the great monkey would never give up. Eventually he let his eyes close for a few seconds. Mancharu, who had been hiding in the topmost branches of a thick tree waiting for this moment, let out a scream of fearful laughter and sprang down on him, breaking his neck with a single blow. Immediately the lake drained away, and all the Huillcas were turned into little hills. But Mancharu was furious; he still had not found Rainbow. He ran wildly round in all directions, growling like thunder. Red lightning flashed from his eyes, and he crushed everything in his reach.

But the girl had changed herself into a ball of wool at the moment he struck, and rolled down to the river along which she escaped. She never dared turn back into a girl in case he found her again, but moves from one stream or lake to another with her new friends the fishes. On rainy days, when she jumps from one river to another, you can see her making an arc of many colours through the sky.

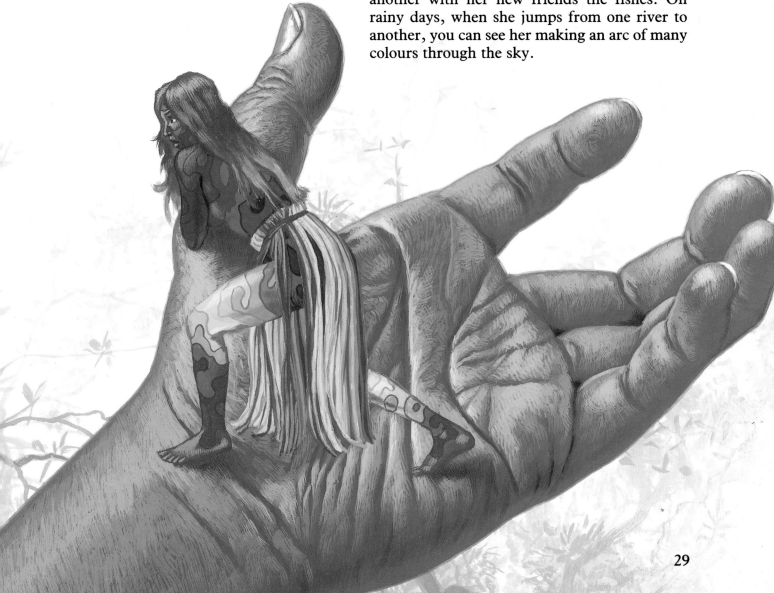

THE STAR PRINCESS

'You are useless!' cried the old Indian to his son. 'Every night someone steals our potatoes, and you do nothing about it. If I were your age I should have caught the thief long ago. Tonight you must watch in the field, and it will be too bad for you if you do not capture him.'

The young man hid under a mound of dry branches and waited for nightfall. But he was overcome by sleep; and when he woke up at dawn he found that a whole row of potatoes had been stolen. He was far too frightened to go home and face his father's anger. He decided to sleep through the day so that the following night he could stay awake; after all, the thief only came in the dark.

When evening came he curled himself up again in his hiding place. Although he did not feel in the least tired, a strange numbness came over him and he fell asleep for a few seconds. When he opened his eyes he could not believe what he saw. The field was crowded with beautiful girls who were busy stealing his potatoes. Their dresses and their long hair were the same colour as the stars, and they laughed and sang as they filled their baskets.

The young man kept his head, and when one of the girls passed close by him he sprang out and caught her by her hair. All the others flew into the sky with their baskets. Within seconds they were back in place as still and shining stars.

The young man begged the girl he had captured to stay on Earth and marry him. But he was sure that his father would be furious and punish her for her theft. He decided to hide his wife in a little hut high in the mountains where his father never went. The star princess never stopped crying. She promised him untold riches in exchange for her freedom, but he would not listen. He loved her so much that he could not live without her.

After several days had gone by, he saw his mother in the distance. He knew that he could not stay hidden for ever. Perhaps when he told his parents how much he loved his wife, they would forgive him. He set out with his star princess. When they met his mother, she was so happy to find her son was safe and sound that she promised to help the young people.

When they reached home, the old Indian was sitting motionless on the ground in front; his arms were crossed on his knees, his lips were pursed and his eyes were half closed. But when he saw the star princess, he got up without a word. Little by little his face softened into a smile, and he waved them into the house. His wife and son were surprised but thankful to see that he was completely charmed by the girl!

The old Indian listened carefully to his son's story. Unbelievable as it seemed, the star

One of the dazzling star princesses is caught, while the rest flee to the sky with their baskets of stolen potatoes.

princess was proof that it was true. 'She can live with us here,' he said at last. 'You are twenty-five, and it is time you chose a wife. The state will give you a plot of ground and you can raise a family. But no one must know who she is. That would bring endless trouble and the governor would not let you marry her. She must hide her shining dress and cover her hair with a shawl. If we are careful, all should go well.'

No one in the village asked awkward questions, and the star princess was so kind that everyone loved her. But although she seemed content, she often looked sad. Each evening, she spent hours gazing at the sky and talking to the stars. One day her mother-in-law asked her what would make her smile. The girl asked for her shining star dress. The old Indian took it from its hiding place and gave it to her. A strange light shone in the girl's eyes. A freezing wind blew through the house and her body shone so brilliantly that the old woman had to close her eyes. When she opened them again the star princess had gone.

The young man was desperate. He climbed high into the mountains where he spent sleepless, hungry days and nights, crying his heart out. One day, a giant condor alighted beside him and said:

'If you give me two llamas, I will take you into the sky to your star.'

The young man ran to his father's flock, and led two llamas back to the condor. Then he climbed on to the giant bird's back and off they flew. They landed by a lake in the sky, near a golden temple. Out came thousands of young girls similar to his wife. He ran over, found his wife among them, and clasped her in his arms. She was delighted to see him. But she knew that if her father the sun or her mother the moon found that she had married a mortal, they would hunt him down. She had to keep his coming a secret.

For more than a year the young man stayed hidden in the star princess's room. He grew pale and weak. One morning, she said:

'You cannot go on living like this; you will die, and I shall never forgive myself. I shall not come home this evening, and you will never see me again. You must live on Earth, not here. Goodbye!'

With these words, she went quickly away without looking back. That evening, she did not return, nor on the following days. The young man realized he had to go back to Earth. He went to the lake shore and called the giant condor. The bird agreed to take him home in exchange for two more llamas, and off they flew.

When he got home, the young Indian decided to hide his adventure from the villagers who would never believe him. So nobody could understand why, every night, he went to his field and cried for hours as he looked at the sky.

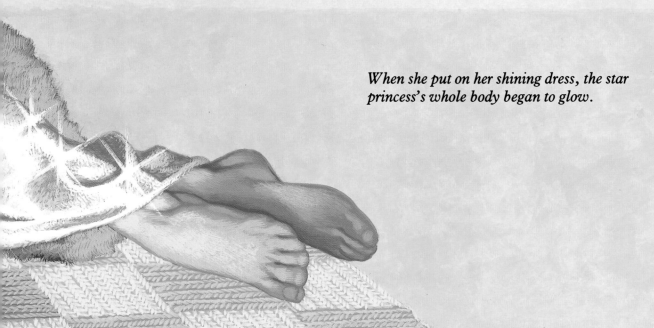

When she put on her shining dress, the star princess's whole body began to glow.

THE BIRTH OF LAKE TITICACA

Long ago, before Lake Titicaca existed, that region was ruled by people so proud that they thought themselves masters of the whole world. Their ruler said that he was the equal of the gods.

One day a group of dirty, tattered Indians came to their city. They preached to the people from every street corner, saying:

'Listen to our warning! Your city is going to be destroyed because the gods are angry with you and want to punish you. But if you go up into the mountains and repent your evil ways, you will be saved.'

At first the proud people mocked the Indians. *They* had no need to repent! As days passed and the Indians went on prophesying disaster, the citizens began to throw stones at them. Only the priests were worried by the warnings. They went to a temple on a mountain nearby to pray.

One afternoon a man saw a strange red glare in the distance. He called his friends, and soon almost all the citizens gathered to look at it. 'Look,' said one of them, 'it is like a cloud of fire.'

'It's the end of the world!' cried another. 'The beggars warned us this would happen.'

'Nonsense,' snapped a third. 'It is simply the reflection of the sun on the clouds. There is nothing to be afraid of.'

But the light drew nearer, and soon a vast red and black mist engulfed the whole city. The sun shone more and more brilliantly, and in the fearful heat everyone fell silent. Suddenly there came a deep roll of thunder; the earth shook violently and buildings came crashing down. The terrified citizens ran in all directions. Then came a deluge of crimson rain; the rivers overflowed their banks and the whole valley was flooded, drowning the city and everyone in it.

Only the priests who had gone to their mountain temple were saved. Their mountain became the island of Titicaca. Later the Incas came there to worship the sun and the moon, and the god of thunder and lightning, and to pray that the sky would never again turn red and black.

LAKE TITICACA

Titicaca is the highest lake in the world. It lies at an altitude of 3,800 metres. It is 220 kilometres long and 112 kilometres wide, and is 200 metres deep in parts. It was formed at the same time as the Andes mountains.

Around the lake are barren mountains and the climate is very harsh but, in spite of these difficult conditions, a comparatively large population of Aymara Indians lived there. They grew potatoes and (a little lower down the mountains) maize and barley, while the lake provided plenty of fish to eat.

The proud people's splendid city was soon to be engulfed by a new lake.

THE THREE EGGS

Long ago when the world was young and barren, Kon created millions of men and women and gave them everything they would need for a good life. But they soon forgot their creator. To punish them, Kon took back all his gifts, and their lives became wretched.

One day a strange man called Pachacamac arrived. He told them that he was the child of the sun and the moon. He overthrew Kon, turned his people into black cats, and made a new man and a new woman. Then he went off; but he had forgotten to give them anything to eat. The man soon died of hunger, and his tearful wife begged the sun to help her. The sun took pity on her. He gave her food, and four days later she gave birth to a son.

Pachacamac was furious. He killed the baby, and turned his body into maize, roots and delicious berries. Pachacamac thought that the people he was about to create would thank him and worship him for ever and ever. However, the sun gave the woman another child. She called him Vichima, and brought him up in hiding.

Years passed, and one day when Vichima was away Pachacamac killed his mother. Then he created a third race of people. When Vichima returned he swore vengeance. He killed Pachacamac's people and called on his father the sun to send down to Earth three giant eggs, one of gold, one of silver, and one of leather. The eggs appeared; the ground shook violently, and the eggs cracked open. From the golden egg came hundreds of noblemen, from the silver egg hundreds of noblewomen, and from the leather egg millions of common people.

Hundreds and thousands of new people streamed from the magic eggs.

THE MIRACLE OF THE FOUNTAIN

Yupanqui knew that he would become the Inca emperor when his father the Inca Viracocha died. One morning he set out to visit the old man. It was a hot day, and on his way Yupanqui stopped to drink from a spring.

As Yupanqui stooped to drink, a huge sheet of crystal slipped into the water. It reflected a strange being; three rays of sunshine shimmered from the nape of his neck; snakes writhed round his arms, and on his forehead was a band like that worn by the Incas. Discs of gold hung from his ears and he was dressed as an emperor. A puma leaned against his legs; another puma rested its paws on his shoulders, and a giant snake lay coiled at his feet.

Yupanqui drew quickly back. He was about to run away in terror when the apparition called his name. It smiled at him and said:

'Do not be frightened, Yupanqui my son; I am your father the sun and I have come to talk to you in secret. I know that you will soon rule the Inca empire and I want you to worship me and sacrifice to me all your life. Make sure that your people also worship me as the greatest of their gods. Then I will protect you and help you to triumph over all difficulties.'

Then the god disappeared, leaving a shining mirror in the fountain. Yupanqui took it and hid it in his clothes before setting off again. He told no one of his strange meeting, but he soon turned a small shrine to the sun into a magnificent temple, and ordered a statue showing the god as he had seen him. When he became emperor, he looked into his mirror whenever he had to take a decision, and the mirror gave him advice and showed him the future.

The god Inti appears to Yupanqui.

37

OLLANTAY AND THE INCA'S DAUGHTER

The great general Ollantay was a Curaca Indian from the village of Tampu. His courage, intelligence, good looks and nobility, as well as the many victories he had won, made him the most famous general in the empire and one of the most brilliant men at its court.

But when Ollantay fell in love with the Inca's daughter Cusy-Coyllur he knew that his love was impossible. The Inca was a god, son of the sun, and all the members of his family were sacred. How could an ordinary mortal dare to marry a goddess? Ollantay had been one of the strongest defenders of the Inca laws but now he rebelled. He knew that the young princess loved him deeply, and so he told her of his love.

Ollantay and Cusy-Coyllur decided to get married in secret. All the court knew what was happening, and the high priest tried in vain to stop them. No one dared tell the Inca himself, for they knew how angry he would be. But after a few months Cusy-Coyllur decided to talk to her father; she was very fond of the old man and she hated lying to him. She told herself that he might perhaps forgive her for breaking one of the empire's strictest laws, and allow her to marry Ollantay officially. Together the general and the princess went to see the Inca. They told him that they loved each other, but not of their secret marriage.

The Inca was furious. He would not speak to his daughter, but ordered that she should be taken to the temple of the virgins of the sun. There she should be strictly guarded, and dedicated to the service of the sun god. The Inca law makers had never imagined that an ordinary Indian might dare to put himself on a level with the gods and think of marrying an Inca princess; there was no punishment laid down for this crime. The Inca could not think of a punishment bad enough. Ollantay was stripped of all his honours and privileges and confined to the court while the Inca thought what to do.

Ollantay could not bear to be separated from his wife. One night he escaped from the court and went to his old army headquarters. He called his captains and said to them:

'I cannot put up with the insults the Inca has heaped on me, nor see my soldiers divided under other generals. I am going to the other side of the Andes mountains to live among the savages there; you will never see me again.'

At this his captains stood up and swore loyalty to their general.

'Whatever you decide, we will follow you,' they told him. 'We will march at your side.'

Ollantay had counted on his soldiers to follow him blindly. He told them his plan. He would rebel against what he considered an unjust law, and march against the capital to compel the Inca to reverse his decision. He felt that his services to his country made him worthy of rights which his birth denied him.

No one had ever questioned the Inca laws, but Ollantay's soldiers followed him without hesitating. They set out at dawn behind him.

Not far from the headquarters another general was setting out with his troops to put down an uprising in the provinces. His name was Ruminahui and, although he was noble and famous, he had always been jealous of Ollantay's glory. He saw the rebellious army and realized that his chance had come. If he could stop Ollantay and take him in chains to the Inca, he would become the hero of the court as he had longed to be.

The Inca's daughter Cusy-Coyllur begs her father to allow her to marry Ollantay.

Ruminahui knew that Ollantay was the best general in the empire and would be hard to beat. He made a cunning plan; he told his troops to follow out of sight and wait for his signal. Then he went by himself to Ollantay's camp. He told the great general that he had come to help him. But the following night Ruminahui rose noiselessly and opened the great gates of the fortress. He gave his troops their signal; they rushed in and slaughtered Ollantay's soldiers as they slept. Ollantay was taken prisoner. At dawn Rumanahui and his soldiers set out for the capital, leading Ollantay in chains between them.

Suddenly a messenger ran up. He told them breathlessly the sad news he was spreading round the country; the old Inca was dead and he had chosen his son Tupac Yupanqui to succeed him. Ollantay wondered what his fate would be. He thought of his wife and the child she had borne since he last saw her. Was it a boy or a girl? Would he be able to see his wife one last time before he died? Would the new Inca have pity on his sister?

At last they reached the court. The audience with Tupac Yupanqui was icy. The Inca had to apply the law, which was the foundation of his empire's strength. Ollantay knew this, but he

asked only to be heard by the new Inca before he died.

'I have always respected the law,' said Ollantay. 'I have risked my life for it many times. But do you not realize that an empire can only be strong if its people know that its laws are founded on justice? Is the law just which forbids a man to love a woman, even if he is worthy of her and they truly love each other, simply because she is of nobler birth? Can a man not earn by his deeds and his will what his birth has not given him? Believe me, your greatness must come not from the strictness with which you enforce your laws but from their justice. Now that I have told you what I believe most sincerely to be the truth, I will submit to my punishment.'

'Stand up,' replied the young Inca. 'I have been thinking for a long time just what you have said. I am going to pardon you and give you the hand of my sister. Your daughter will be recognized too, and I hope that all three of you will live happily at my court.'

It was exactly mid-day when the Inca said these words, and when he left the palace it seemed that the sun shone particularly brilliantly, just as if it were telling him that he had done right.

Ollantay's soldiers are surprised and killed by Ruminahui's troops.

41

▷ TITU THE GREAT ◁

The Indians believed that the laws which ruled the Inca empire had been made by Titu the Great. He was also known as Pachacutec, which meant 'Reformer of the World'. Titu ruled over a great kingdom but he was also – and more importantly – the direct descendant of the sun god. He was such a wise and good emperor that he was the most admired and worshipped of all the Inca deities.

Pachacutec greatly increased the size of the kingdom which he inherited from his father. The tribes around wanted to weaken their powerful neighbour and often attacked his kingdom, but Pachacutec was as good a general as he was a law maker and he always gained the victory.

Then came a time when Pachacutec thought that his day was done. He was threatened by a large, well-trained army that had won many battles. He was very worried, and each night in his dreams he called on the great god Viracocha to help him. The god told him to trust in him, and to wait. Each morning the Inca made splendid offerings to Viracocha and prayed to him.

One night the Inca woke up with a start. Viracocha was there in front of him; he looked like a man but when he began to speak his voice sounded strange.

'My son,' he said, 'tomorrow your enemies will attack. Your mission on Earth is not yet finished, so I will help you to conquer them. I know that you have not enough soldiers, so I will send you some more.' Then the great god disappeared in a golden cloud.

The Inca could hardly believe what he had heard, but he had such trust in Viracocha that he set out at dawn at the head of his army to meet the enemy. On the battleground the ranks of enemy soldiers stretched far into the distance. The Inca turned and looked at his few hundred soldiers with dismay. Suddenly he heard the sound of drums. At that moment the sun appeared from behind the mountain top, and Pachacutec saw that on the slopes of the mountains surrounding the battleground were thousands of soldiers whose weapons shone like stars. No one had ever seen such troops before.

The battle lasted until mid-day; hundreds of Pachacutec's enemies were killed or taken prisoner. When they saw that one of their greatest generals had been killed, the survivors abandoned the struggle and fled in disarray.

At last the Inca could complete the mission with which his father the sun had entrusted him; to reform the Inca world. And when he died, he alone of all the Inca emperors had the right to sit among the gods.

PACHACUTEC'S REFORMS
Pachacutec Inca Yupanqui became Inca emperor in AD 1438. He was responsible for enlarging the empire and for its strict organization. He ordered that all the Indians under his rule learned the Inca language; no official duty could be given to anyone who did not speak it perfectly. He believed that everyone should work hard, and made laws to punish laziness; but he instituted a rest day after every nine working days. Laws regulated work and food, feast days and marriages, sacrifices and clothing.

Under Pachacutec every aspect of life was controlled by the state, but even the old, the sick and the disabled were looked after.

At dawn each day, the Inca made offerings to the great god Viracocha.

THE INCAS AND THEIR EMPIRE

When the Spaniard Pizarro and his soldiers discovered the Inca empire in AD 1532, it stretched for some 3200 kilometres along the west coast of South America, from what is now Colombia in the north to Chile in the south. To the east rose the Andes mountains. The empire covered an area of some 611,000 square kilometres – as large as France, the Netherlands, Switzerland and Italy together.

The Incas were a group of related families from Cuzco, high up in the Andes. They had arrived there around 1100, under their leader Manco Capac, but they only began to build their empire under Pachacutec Inca Yupanqui in the mid 15th century. Although the Inca empire lasted only a hundred years, it united all the different peoples under one ruthlessly efficient system, in which everything was controlled by the state.

The peoples of the area are generally known as Indians. In early times they were hunters, but they learned how to tame animals and grow crops to become farmers. On the coasts large fishing villages grew up. None of these people knew how to write, so we only know about them from the objects they made, including pottery and skilfully woven cloth as well as wonderful golden ornaments and objects.

The Incas themselves did not know how to write. Most of what we know about them comes from Spanish accounts. The Spanish questioned them closely about their history, but were never able to sort out what was history and what was legend. It seems that Pachacutec Inca Yupanqui came to the throne in 1438, and began to conquer the neighbouring tribes and bring them under Inca rule. His son Topa Inca Yupanqui carried on the expansion of the empire, conquering the powerful Chimu people of the north coast. Pachacutec and Topa were responsible for the system of organizing the empire, which made it possible for the comparatively small number of Incas – members of the

The approximate area of the Inca empire at its greatest extent.

ruling family – to control such a vast area.

Organizing the empire

The Inca emperor was looked on as the direct descendant of the sun. He was all powerful and his word was law. The custom was for him to marry his sister, the Coya, and he also had a number of secondary wives. The Inca emperor chose who was to succeed him, usually one of the Coya's sons; but in this case the other Incas had the right to object to his choice.

All the officials of the empire, including priests and army officers, were members of the Inca family in the early day's of the empire. But as it grew larger there were not enough of them, so the Inca decreed that everyone who spoke the Inca language, Quechua, and had the same customs, should become Incas. They had many privileges; they travelled in litters rather than on foot, and could wear gold ornaments and much finer clothes than the ordinary people. The chiefs of conquered areas, who were known as curacas, made up a second group of noblemen.

The Incas were brilliant organizers. They were able to conquer their vast empire because their army was well trained, well armed, and well supplied with food and medicines from special storehouses. All the people they conquered were made to follow the same laws.

Working for the state

All the land in the Inca empire belonged to the state; it was divided into three parts. Crops from one part went to the gods, to provide offerings to the gods and food for the priests. Crops from the second part went into the emperor's storehouses, to provide for him, his officials, soldiers and craftsmen. These storehouses also provided for those who could not look after themselves, including widows and orphans, sick people and the old. Crops from the rest of the land went to the peasants. Each family was allotted enough for its needs every year. The peasants worked all the land – first they looked after the fields of the gods, then those of the emperor, and finally their own.

In the same way, the llamas and alpacas that grazed in the highlands were divided among the gods, the emperor and the peasants. Wool from the royal storehouses was handed out to the people to make clothes and rugs.

Everyone under Inca rule had their own place in the Inca society. There were rules which said what children up to the age of 9 should be doing, others for children of 9 to 16, and so on. Specially talented or good-looking boys might be taken to be trained to work in the temples, to be servants of the emperor and his nobles, or to be supervisors. The most beautiful girls were taken at about 10 years old; some of these 'chosen women' were trained to become wives for the emperor and the Incas; some, known as the virgins of the sun, had special duties in the temples.

The Incas had no money system. Instead of paying taxes, men between the ages of 25 and 50 had special duties (the mita) to perform, which included working for the state as messengers, miners, builders or soldiers. This mita was in addition to their work in the fields.

At 25 most people married; the state gave them land to work, a house to live in, and new clothes to wear. For the first year they were exempt from the mita. More land was added each time they had a baby.

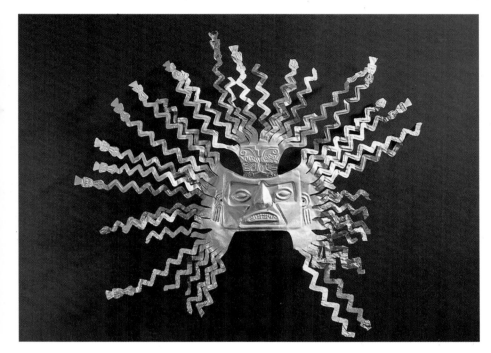

This golden mask is a symbol of the sun. The Inca empire had many highly skilled craftsmen, in particular metal workers and potters.

Reed boats like those found on Lake Titicaca today were used in Inca times.

When a man was unable to do a full day's work, he was classified by the state as 'old' and given lighter tasks such as collecting brushwood. Disabled people were also given lighter work. The old, the sick and the disabled had all their basic needs looked after by the state; under Inca rule, there were no beggars.

Keeping records

Although the Incas had no system of writing, they devised a way of keeping detailed records. This involved a *quipu*, a long piece of string to which were attached shorter, knotted strings of different colours. No one knows how to 'read' a quipu today, so their records are lost; but it seems that the knots represented numbers and the colours different objects. Detailed records were kept of each province, including its people, animals, land and mines, and of the storehouses and everything in them. These records were regularly checked by state officials.

Crops and herds

The lands of the Inca empire varied from the desert area behind the coast to the high Andes mountains, and the dense forests of the west which few people dared to enter. Valleys were fertile, and the Incas built terraces and irrigation canals on the mountain slopes so that they could grow crops there too. Maize and potatoes were the most important crops; fruit and cotton were also grown.

Herds of llamas and alpacas grazed on the mountain grasslands. Most belonged to the gods or the emperor; no peasant was allowed to own more than ten llamas. Llamas were used as pack animals; their wool was coarse and was used for such things as sacks and ropes. Finer wool came from alpacas, which were regularly shorn. The finest cloth came from the wool of vicunas, wild relatives of the llama that were caught and sheared each year. These animals also provided meat and leather. Ducks and guinea pigs were kept for meat. Dogs were tamed as pets and for hunting deer and the small wild llamas called guanacos. Hunting – like everything else – was strictly regulated, and done only with official permission.

Food and clothing

Soups and stews made from vegetables formed the major part of the Indians' diet. Hot chilli peppers and herbs were used as flavourings. The Indians ate fish when it was available, but not much meat. They cooked in clay pots over fires of llama dung, for wood was very scarce. In warmer lowland areas they grew avocados, tomatoes, beans, peanuts, and fruits including bananas. Honey was used as a sweetener. The ruling Incas ate well, and food from all

The Incas made their last stand against the conquering Spaniards at Machu Picchu, high up in the Andes.

over the empire was rushed to Cuzco by relays of runners.

The favourite drink was chicha, a sort of beer made from fermented maize and other vegetables. Large quantities of it were drunk at festivals.

Indian clothes were simple. They were made of cotton in the warmer, coastal region, and elsewhere of wool. Men wore a tunic over a loin cloth; women wore a long tunic tied round the waist. Both wore cloaks. The Incas wore more elaborate clothes of finer wool. They were decorated with geometric patterns and sometimes with brightly coloured feathers. The Incas also wore ornaments of gold, silver and precious stones; these included large gold earrings.

Travel

Two main paved highways ran through the Inca empire from north to south, one in the mountains and the other along the coast. These were linked by a network of smaller tracks. Rope bridges spanned deep ravines, and in places steps were cut up steep mountain slopes. The Incas, like other South American peoples, did not have wheels. They used llamas as pack animals; important people travelled in litters and everyone else walked.

Messages were carried throughout the empire by relays of messengers, who ran as fast as they could between small shelters about 1.5 kilometres apart. They could also carry small packages.

Religion

The most important Inca gods are described on pages 22 and 23. The people conquered by the Incas had to worship the Inca gods, but they were allowed to worship their traditional gods as well.

As the myths show, religion played a very important part in everyday life. The most important official was the high priest of the sun, who was the brother or uncle of the emperor and was based at Cuzco. He was helped by a council of nine priests.

Every town had its own temple, sometimes elaborately decorated and containing golden objects. There were also large numbers of lesser temples, shrines and holy places where the people worshipped and sacrificed. They made offerings of food and animals, and very poor people could even offer their eyelashes if they had nothing else.

The Incas believed that sins offended the gods and called down punishments, so confession was important. They were very superstitious, and any unusual events were seen as omens. A howling dog foretold death. The priests examined the entrails of sacrificed animals for omens.

Once a year in the most important temples two young children were sacrificed. Human sacrifices might also be made in times of serious trouble, such as famine, and as many as 200 boys and girls were sacrificed when a new emperor came to power.

The conquest

In 1532 the Spaniard Francisco Pizarro landed on the coast of the Inca empire. He and his companions had heard of the Incas' fabulous golden treasures. The Inca Atahualpa welcomed the Spanish who trapped and captured him. Although he gave them an enormous ransom in gold to buy his freedom, they killed him. The Incas resisted for some years; probably they withdrew to Machu Picchu high in the mountains. The last Inca leader, Tupac Amaru, gave himself up to the Spaniards in 1572, when he and his family were executed.

The Spanish were cruel and ruthless rulers. They swept away the Inca laws and regulations and turned the people into slaves, forcing many of them to work in the mines until they dropped dead. The peasants became wretchedly poor, while the Spaniards looted and destroyed all they came across in their greedy search for gold.

Today the descendants of the Incas live in the Andes mountains. They still speak Quechua, the Inca language; they herd their llamas and build their rope bridges.

Archaeologists are excavating Inca ruins and examining the objects they made, so that we can learn more and more about their immense but short-lived empire.

A modern Peruvian Indian sells her wares beneath an Inca wall in Cuzco.

INDEX